Illustrated by Debbie Pinkney
Adapted by Erin Lyons

Louis Weber, C.E.O., Publications International, Ltd.
7373 North Cicero Avenue, Lincolnwood, Illinois 60712

Ground Floor, 59 Gloucester Place, London W1U 8JJ

Customer Service: 1-800-595-8484 or customer_service@pilbooks.com

www.pilbooks.com

8 7 6 5 4 3 2 1

ISBN-13: 978-1-4127-3183-6
ISBN-10: 1-4127-3183-6

Akili came home from jungle school very excited. "I made a new friend!" she said. "Her name is Maarifa. Can she come over?"

Akili's mom was very happy. She had been worried that Akili wasn't playing enough with the other young elephants. "Of course you can! Why don't you bring your new friend over tonight?"

"Hooray!" Akili said and rushed off to tell her new friend the good news.

But when Akili's new friend appeared for dinner, the other elephants were shocked to see a mouse, not another young elephant. "Eek!" the elephants cried, and hid in the bushes. Akili and Maarifa were confused.

"Why are they afraid of you?" asked Akili.

"Maybe we should eat at my house," Maarifa squeaked.

But at Maarifa's house the same thing happened. Maarifa's family was terrified when they saw an elephant outside the door. All of the mice quickly scurried out of sight.

The two friends were very puzzled.

"I don't understand why our families are afraid of each other," said Akili.

"We must find out," said Maarifa.

Akili asked her mom why elephants were afraid of mice. Akili's mom said, "They sneak up on us and squeak to scare us. They play mean tricks."

Maarifa asked her family why they were afraid of elephants. "Elephants are dangerous. They step on us and trample our homes," the mice said.

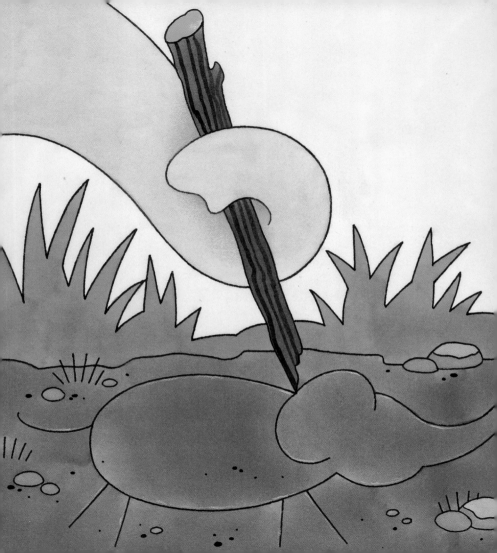

"This is not right!" Akili and Maarifa agreed. "Just because we're different doesn't mean we can't be friends!"

The two friends decided to show their families that mice and elephants could get along. They drew pictures in the dirt to show how much elephants and mice would look alike if they were the same size.

But their families wouldn't listen. "Mice and elephants are just too different," their mothers said. "You can't play with each other. It's much too dangerous."

This made Akili and Maarifa very sad. They both began to cry.

Akili and Maarifa's mothers heard their children crying and ran to dry their eyes with leaves. When the two mothers saw each other, they began to laugh.

"We're not so different after all," Maarifa's mother said.

"You're right," Akili's mother agreed. "Mice and elephants *can* get along."

Tolerance

Tolerance means accepting other people, even if they are different from you. Maarifa and Akili looked very different from one another. That is why their families didn't like each other at first. But then they learned that they weren't so different after all. When you show tolerance, it's easy to make new friends.